# Johannes Brahms

## Double Concerto
## for Violin, Cello and Orchestra
## in A minor / a-Moll
### Op. 102

Edited by / Herausgegeben von
Hans Gál

EULENBURG

EAS 164
ISBN 978-3-7957-6564-4
ISMN 979-0-2002-2554-9

© 2010 Ernst Eulenburg & Co GmbH, Mainz
for Europe excluding the British Isles
Ernst Eulenburg Ltd, London
for all other countries
Edition based on Eulenburg Study Score ETP 723
CD ℗ & © 1995 Naxos Rights International Ltd

Ernst Eulenburg Ltd
48 Great Marlborough Street
London W1F 7BB

# Contents / Inhalt

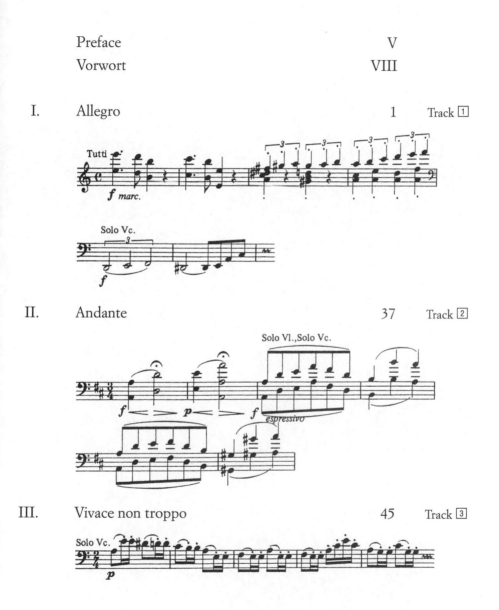

# Preface

**Composed: 1887 in Thun**
**First performance: 18 October 1887 in Cologne, soloists: Joseph Joachim (violin), Robert Hausmann (cello); conductor: Johannes Brahms**
**Original publisher: Simrock, Berlin, 1888**
**Instrumentation: 2 Flutes, 2 Oboes, 2 Clarinets, 2 Bassoons –**
**4 Horns, 2 Trumpets – Timpani – Strings**
**Duration: ca. 33 minutes**

The genesis of Brahms's Double Concerto – his last concerto and, indeed, his last orchestral composition – is poorly documented. All that we can say for certain is that Brahms wrote it down during the summer of 1887, which he spent in Thun on the shores of the lake that gives the village its name. He completed work on the draft in mid-July and by the beginning of August had put the finishing touches to the full score. His early biographer Max Kalbeck claims that Brahms fell back on material originally intended for a fifth symphony,[1] but this claim is unsupported by any evidence and must be regarded as pure speculation.

Brahms's decision to write a concerto was almost certainly inspired by one of his friends, the cellist Robert Hausmann, who had taught the instrument at the Royal Academy of Music in Berlin since 1876 and who had joined the famous Joachim Quartet three years later. Brahms thought very highly of his playing, which combined virtuosity with great musical sensitivity, and had already written his Second Cello Sonata in F major Op. 99 for Hausmann. Composed in the summer of 1886, it had received its first performance in Vienna in the November of that year, when Hausmann had been accompanied by Brahms himself. It is conceivable that Brahms had already promised to write a cello concerto for Hausmann as early as 1884, because on 4 December 1884 we find one of the composer's female friends, the pianist Elisabet von Herzogenberg, writing to ask him: 'Is it true that you are writing a cello concerto?'[2] It is impossible to say if Brahms had already noted down any of the sketches for this concerto by this date, but there is no doubt that he initially intended to write a cello concerto. This also explains the lines that Brahms sent to Hausmann by way of an apology on 10 August 1887: 'But you would have taken it with an extremely bad grace if I had added a solo violin to a cello concerto!'[3]

---

[1]  Max Kalbeck, *Johannes Brahms*, 4 vols. (Berlin, 3/1912–21), IV, 64
[2]  Max Kalbeck (ed.), *Johannes Brahms im Briefwechsel mit Heinrich und Elisabet von Herzogenberg*, 2 vols. (Berlin, 1907), II, 43 (letter from Elisabet von Herzogenberg to Johannes Brahms, 4 December 1884).
[3]  Quoted by Peter Jost, '"Gewissermaßen ein Versöhnungswerk": Doppelkonzert A-Moll, op. 102', *Johannes Brahms: Das symphonische Werk. Einführung, Deutung, Wirkung*, ed. Renate Ulm (Kassel and Munich, 1996), 172.

If Brahms changed his original plans and instead of writing a cello concerto composed a double concerto for violin and cello – a combination of instruments hitherto unrepresented in the great concerto literature of the 19th century – then he owed this change of heart to the violin virtuoso, Joseph Joachim, who was the leader of the string quartet that bore his name and the director of the Royal Academy of Music in Berlin, where he also held a professorial position. Brahms and Joachim had been close friends since the 1850s but had had a falling out in 1880 in the wake of Joachim's marital problems, problems that had been caused by the violinist's morbid jealousy, prompting Brahms to side with Joachim's wife, the contralto Amalie Joachim née Schneeweiß, who was unjustly accused of adultery. (A letter that Brahms wrote to her in December 1880 played an important role in her separation from her husband four years later.) For decades the two men had maintained an intimate correspondence, but this now dried up, and for a time they avoided each other altogether, notably when Brahms visited Berlin in early 1884. Every trivial action, such as the refusal to shake the other man's hand in 1883, rankled as a mortifying insult.

In the light of all these tensions, Brahms was bound to find himself in a dilemma in 1887: if he wrote a cello concerto for the cellist of the Joachim Quartet, as he had promised to do, then the leader of the quartet would have felt that he had been passed over and would have felt insulted all over again. There was really only one solution to satisfy and pacify both parties: that of a double concerto for violin and cello. In a letter to Clara Schumann, Brahms described this as 'an amusing idea',[4] while his publisher Fritz Simrock was told only a few days later that it was the composer's 'latest folly'.[5] The previous month, he had written to Joachim himself: 'Prepare yourself for a little shock! I've recently been unable to resist the idea of a concerto for violin and violoncello, however much I've tried to talk myself out of it.'[6] Joachim had no reason to complain that of the two solo instruments the cello is accorded preferential treatment. After all, his own part includes a number of specific allusions to him: in the third movement, for example, the Hungarian elements recall Joachim's Violin Concerto 'in ungarischer Weise' Op. 11, while the F–A–E motif is a musical acrostic associated with the much younger Brahms and his motto 'Frei, aber einsam' (Free, but lonely). The main theme of the opening movement, finally, recalls the beginning of the Violin Concerto No. 22 in A minor by Giovanni Battista Viotti, a favourite piece of Joachim's. Clara Schumann was in no doubt that 'this concerto is a work of reconciliation – this is the first time in years that Joachim and Brahms have spoken to each other again'.[7]

It comes as no surprise to learn that Brahms asked both Joachim and Hausmann to look through the cello part and, where necessary, to suggest changes to it. After all, Brahms was

[4] Berthold Litzmann (ed.), *Clara Schumann – Johannes Brahms: Briefe aus den Jahren 1853–1896*, 2 vols. (Leipzig, 1927), II, 322 (undated letter from Johannes Brahms to Clara Schumann, [between 5 and 15 August 1887]).
[5] Max Kalbeck (ed.), *Johannes Brahms: Briefe an Fritz Simrock*, 4 vols. (Berlin, 1917–18), III, 158 (letter from Johannes Brahms to Fritz Simrock, 23 August 1887).
[6] Andreas Moser (ed.), *Johannes Brahms im Briefwechsel mit Joseph Joachim*, 2 vols. (Berlin 1907–8), II, 215 (letter from Johannes Brahms to Joseph Joachim, [24 July 1887]).
[7] Berthold Litzmann (ed.), *Clara Schumann: Ein Künstlerleben. Nach Tagebüchern und Briefen*, 3 vols. (Leipzig, 1920), III, 496 (diary entry of 21 September 1887).

a pianist and in spite of his experience of instrumentation he was conscious of the fact that, as he told Clara Schumann, there was a difference between

> writing for instruments whose character and sound you may happen to have in your head and that you can hear only in your mind's ear and those that you know thoroughly, much as I myself know the piano, where I know exactly what I am writing and why I am writing in such and such a way.[8]

Brahms's idea of playing through the new work and trying it out must have been bound up with this uncertainty, and both Hausmann and Joachim must have agreed to it. They decided to meet at Clara Schumann's holiday home in Baden-Baden. Clara herself was present. Brahms and Hausmann played through the piece on 20 September, and Joachim joined them the next day. Many of the changes that found their way into the 1888 edition of the full score must date back to these run-throughs and were no doubt tried out at this time. A trial performance of the work was held in the Louis Quinze Ballroom in Baden-Baden on 23 September with the local spa orchestra. One of those who was present on this occasion later recalled that

> the musicians, some of whom were outstanding artists in their own right, regarded it as a refreshing change from their daily routine to play under Brahms's direction. Joachim and Hausmann were paying a flying visit as soloists, and in the front row of the informally dressed audience we noted the venerable figure of an elderly woman bathed in the aura of eternal youth – Frau Klara Schumann. The autograph score of the new work lay open before her on a music stand.[9]

The work was 'played through twice in succession under Brahms's energetic direction' and earned the composer 'not only the tumultuous applause of his friends but also a fanfare from the orchestra'.[10]

The official first performance took place in the Gürzenich-Saal in Cologne on 18 October 1887 under Brahms's direction and proved a huge success, even if some of the reviewers complained about the inaccessibility of the music. But this criticism can also be seen in a more positive light, for it implies that at each new hearing the work reveals new aspects.

Klaus Döge
Translation: Stewart Spencer

---

[8] Litzmann, *Clara Schumann* (note 4), II, 322 (undated letter from Johannes Brahms to Clara Schumann, [between 5 and 15 August 1887]).
[9] Kalbeck, *Johannes Brahms* (note 1), IV, 74 (The memoirist was Gustav Manz.)
[10] Kalbeck, *Johannes Brahms* (note 1), IV, 75

# Vorwort

**Komponiert: 1887 in Thun**
**Uraufführung: 18. Oktober 1887 in Köln; Solisten: Joseph Joachim**
**(Violine), Robert Hausmann (Cello); Dirigent: Johannes Brahms**
**Originalverlag: Simrock, Berlin, 1888**
**Orchesterbesetzung: 2 Flöten, 2 Oboen, 2 Klarinetten, 2 Fagotte –**
**4 Hörner, 2 Trompeten – Pauken – Streicher**
**Spieldauer: etwa 33 Minuten**

Die Entstehungsgeschichte des Doppelkonzertes, jener letzten Konzert- und Orchester-
komposition von Johannes Brahms überhaupt, ist nur spärlich dokumentiert. Feststeht, dass
Brahms das Opus 102 im Sommer 1887 in Thun am Thuner See niederschrieb, wo er seine
damaligen Sommerferien verbrachte. Mitte Juli war die Komposition abgeschlossen, Anfang
August wurde die Partitur beendet. Dass er dabei, wie der Brahms-Biograph Max Kalbeck
behauptete[1], auf Material zurückgriff, das ursprünglich für eine fünfte Symphonie gedacht
war, lässt sich durch keine Quelle belegen und muss als pure Spekulation betrachtet werden.

Die Anregung zur Komposition eines Werkes der Gattung „Konzert" dürfte von Robert
Hausmann ausgegangen sein. Dieser mit Brahms befreundete Cellist wirkte seit 1876 als
Lehrer an der Königlichen Hochschule für Musik in Berlin und wurde 1879 Mitglied des
berühmten Joachim-Quartetts. Sein Spiel, seine virtuose, stets aber musikalisch einfühlsame
Art des Vortrages schätzte Brahms hoch ein, und für ihn komponierte er denn auch im
Sommer 1886 seine zweite Sonate für Violoncello, F-Dur op. 99, die er im November 1886
zusammen mit dem Berliner Cellisten in Wien uraufführte. Auf seine Bitte hin ein Cellokonzert zu schreiben, hatte Brahms möglicherweise bereits im Jahre 1884 versprochen, denn am
4. Dezember 1884 fragte die mit dem Komponisten befreundete Künstlerin Elisabet von
Herzogenberg: „Ist es wahr, daß Sie ein Cellokonzert schreiben […]?"[2] Ob Brahms sich
bereits damals zu diesem Konzert irgendwelche Skizzen notiert hatte, lässt sich nicht beant-
worten, aber dass es seine ursprüngliche Idee und Intention gewesen war, ein Cellokonzert zu
komponieren, geht daraus zweifelsohne hervor. Das erklärt Brahms' gleichsam entschuldi-
gende Zeilen an Hausmann vom 10. August 1887: „oder aber Sie hätten es höchst ungnädig
vermerkt dass ich zu einem V'Cell-Concert gar noch eine Solo-Violine nehme!"[3]

[1]  Max Kalbeck, *Johannes Brahms*, 4 Bde., 3. Auflage, Berlin 1912–1921, Bd. IV, S. 64.
[2]  *Johannes Brahms im Briefwechsel mit Heinrich und Elisabet von Herzogenberg*, hg. von Max Kalbeck, Bd. 2, Berlin
     1907, S. 43.
[3]  Zitiert nach Peter Jost, „„Gewissermaßen ein Versöhnungswerk'. Doppelkonzert A-Moll, op. 102", in: *Johannes
     Brahms – Das symphonische Werk. Einführung, Deutung, Wirkung*, hg. von Renate Ulm, Kassel-München 1996,
     S. 172.

Ursache für die Konzeptionsänderung vom ursprünglich geplanten Violoncello-Solokonzert hin zum Doppelkonzert für Violine und Violoncello – für eine bis dahin in der großen Konzertkomposition des 19. Jahrhunderts nicht vertretene Besetzung – war der Geigenvirtuose, Quartettprimarius, Professor und Direktor der Berliner Musikhochschule, Joseph Joachim, mit dem Brahms von den 1850er Jahren an eine enge Freundschaft verband. Im Zusammenhang mit Joachims aus krankhafter Eifersucht hervorgerufenen Eheproblemen, in denen Brahms Partei für die unbegründet der Untreue bezichtigte Ehefrau, die Altistin Amalie Joachim, geborene Schneeweiß, ergriff (ein diesbezüglicher Brief von ihm vom Dezember 1880 spielte bei der Scheidung zugunsten Amalie Joachims 1884 eine wichtige Rolle), kam es 1880 jedoch zum Bruch dieser Freundschaft. Der jahrzehntelange und sehr vertraut geführte Briefwechsel erlosch für längere Zeit; man ging sich (wie etwa bei Brahms' Berlin-Besuch Anfang 1884) aus dem Wege, und jede Kleinigkeit (wie etwa ein nicht angenommener Handschlag im Jahre 1883) wurde als kränkende Beleidigung angesehen.

Angesichts all dieser Spannungen muss Brahms' Schaffenssituation des Jahres 1887 wie eine Zwickmühle erscheinen: Denn hätte er, wie versprochen, ein Cello-Konzert für Hausmann, den Cellisten des Joachim-Quartetts (!), komponiert, hätte sich dessen Primarius übergangen, zurückgesetzt und aufs Neue tief verletzt fühlen können. Es blieb, um beide Beteiligten gleichermaßen zufrieden und ruhig zu stellen, eigentlich nur ein „Ausweg": der eines Doppelkonzertes für Violine und Violoncello. Als „lustigen Einfall" hat Brahms diese Lösung Clara Schumann gegenüber beschrieben;[4] als „meine letzte Dummheit" bezeichnete er das Opus 102 in einem Brief an den Verleger Simrock;[5] und an Joachim schrieb er am 24. Juli 1887: „Aber mache Dich auf einen kleinen Schreck gefasst! Ich konnte nämlich derzeit den Einfällen zu einem Konzert für Violine und Violoncello nicht widerstehen, sosehr ich es mir auch immer wieder auszureden versuchte."[6] Darüber, dass Brahms in seinem Doppelkonzert das Solocello der Geige gegenüber etwas bevorzugt behandelte, hatte Joachim keinen Grund, sich zu beklagen. Gab es doch in seinem Part eine Reihe von speziellen „Joachim-Andeutungen": etwa die auf Joachims Violinkonzert in ungarischer Weise op. 11 anspielenden Ungarismen in Satz III; oder das Zitieren des F-A-E-Motivs, ein musikalisches Akrostichon, das auf die Devise „Frei, aber einsam" des jungen Joachim hinweist; oder die zitatartige Anspielung im Hauptthema des 1. Satzes auf den Beginn des Violinkonzertes Nr. 22 a-Moll von Giovanni Battista Viotti, das ein Lieblingsstück von Joachim war. Für Clara Schumann lag es offen auf der Hand: „Es ist dies Concert gewissermaßen ein Versöhnungswerk – Joachim und Brahms haben sich seit Jahren zum ersten Mal wieder gesprochen."[7]

Dass Brahms Joachim und parallel dazu auch Hausmann bat, sich die Solostimme durchzusehen und ihm – wo nötig – hinsichtlich der Solofiguren Änderungsvorschläge zu unterbrei-

---

[4]  Brahms an Clara Schumann, zwischen 5. und 15. August 1887, in: *Clara Schumann – Johannes Brahms: Briefe aus den Jahren 1853 bis 1896*, hg. von Berthold Litzmann, 2 Bde., Leipzig 1927, Bd. 2, S. 322.

[5]  Brief vom 23. August 1887, in: *Johannes Brahms. Briefe an Fritz Simrock*, hg. von Max Kalbeck, Bd. 3, Berlin 1918, S. 158.

[6]  Zitiert nach: *Johannes Brahms-Briefwechsel*, 16 Bde., Berlin 1906–1921, Nachdruck Tutzing 1974, Bd. VI, S. 230f.

[7]  Eintrag ins Tagebuch vom 21. September 1887, zitiert nach: Berthold Litzmann, *Clara Schumann. Ein Künstlerleben. Nach Tagebüchern und Briefen*, Bd. 3, Leipzig 1920, S. 496.

ten, muss nicht verwundern: Brahms war Pianist und trotz aller Instrumentationserfahrung war ihm bewusst, wie er damals Clara Schumann gegenüber meinte, dass es etwas anderes sei,

> für Instrumente zu schreiben, deren Art und Klang man nur so beiläufig im Kopf hat, die man nur im Geist hört – oder für ein Instrument zu schreiben, das man durch und durch kennt, wie ich das Klavier, wo ich durchaus weiß, was ich schreibe und warum ich so und so schreibe.[8]

Seine Idee eines Durchspielens und Probens des neuen Werkes dürfte damit zusammen-gehangen haben und wurde sowohl von Hausmanns als auch von Joachims Seite her zuge-stimmt. Als gemeinsamer Treffpunkt ergab sich das Sommerhaus von Clara Schumann in Baden-Baden, die dabei anwesend war. Am 20. September probte Brahms mit Hausmann am Klavier, einen Tag später kam Joachim hinzu. Manche Abänderung in der Partitur, die in den Druck von 1888 einfloss, dürfte auf dieses Proben zurückgehen und wohl damals vor-genommen worden sein. Am 23. September schließlich fand im Ballsaal „Louis quinze" eine Versuchsaufführung des Werkes mit dem Baden-Badener Kur-Orchester statt. Ein Anwesen-der erinnert sich:

> Die Musiker, zum Teil hervorragende Künstler, empfanden es als Erquickung im gleich-mäßigen Tagesdienst, einmal unter Brahms' Leitung zu spielen. Joachim und Hausmann waren als Solisten herbeigeeilt, und in der ersten Reihe der zwanglos sitzenden Hörer bemerkte man die ehrwürdige Gestalt einer Greisin, die der Schimmer ewiger Künstler-jugend umwebte – Frau Klara Schumann. Vor ihr auf einem Notenpult lag die Handschrift des neuen Werkes […].[9]

Das Konzert, „das zweimal hintereinander unter Brahms' energischer Leitung gespielt wurde", brachte „dem Tondichter nebst dem rauschenden Freundesbeifall einen Orchester-tusch ein."[10]

Die offizielle Uraufführung unter Brahms' Leitung am 18. Oktober 1887 im Kölner Gürze-nich-Saal stellte einen großen Erfolg dar, auch wenn in manchen Rezensionen die schwere Eingänglichkeit der Musik bemängelt wurde. Positiv gewendet aber bedeutet dies nichts anderes, als bei jedem Hören des Werkes Neues zu entdecken.

Klaus Doege

---

[8] Brahms an Clara Schumann, zwischen 5. und 15. August 1887, in: *Clara Schumann – Johannes Brahms: Briefe aus den Jahren 1853 bis 1896*, hg. von Berthold Litzmann, 2 Bde., Leipzig 1927, Bd. 2, S. 322.
[9] Max Kalbeck, a. a. O., S. 74.
[10] Ebda., S. 75.

# Double Concerto for Violin, Cello and Orchestra

Johannes Brahms
(1833–1897)
Op. 102

EAS 164

© 2010 Ernst Eulenburg Ltd, London
and Ernst Eulenburg & Co GmbH, Mainz

4

14

23

EAS 164

38

EAS 164

III. Vivace non troppo

52

54

62

**Poco meno Allegro**

**Poco meno Allegro**